IMAGES OF ENGLAND

MINING IN CORNWALL

VOLUME SEVEN
SOUTH CROFTY MINE –
THE EAST POOL & AGAR MINES

In memory of my late grandfather, James Henry Bullen (1842–1915). He was the resident engineer for Hocking & Loam at the Consolidated Mines and the United Mines, Gwennap. Later he became chief engineer at the Carn Brea & Tincroft Mines, from where he retired in 1907.

IMAGES OF ENGLAND

MINING IN CORNWALL

VOLUME SEVEN

SOUTH CROFTY MINE – THE EAST POOL & AGAR MINES

L.J. BULLEN

The
History
Press

First published in 2004 by Tempus Publishing

Reprinted in 2010 by
The History Press
The Mill, Brimscombe Port,
Stroud, Gloucestershire, GL5 2QG
www.thehistorypress.co.uk

Reprinted 2013

British Library Cataloguing in Publication Data.
A catalogue record for this book is available from the British Library.

ISBN 978 0 7524 3249 6

Typesetting and origination by Tempus Publishing.
Printed and bound in Great Britain by
Marston Book Services Limited, Oxfordshire.

Contents

Acknowledgements

I have been helped in many ways by the following members of my family: my wife, who has once again rendered invaluable help in proof-reading, and my daughter, Anne Smith, and her husband, Robert, for their large input in the computer field, which greatly facilitates the production process. I am also indebted to Brian Errington for his support in photographic processing and to W.S. Uren, the grandson of the late Billy House.

East Pool & Agar Ltd, *c.* 1912.

Introduction

The Central Mining District of Cornwall is by far the most concentrated area of mines in the county. It also claims the deepest and more productive mining enterprises. Once again this volume is drawn from a very comprehensive collection of Cornish mining photographs. It portrays scenes at three mines which, like many others, were household names at one time. The mines of the district employed many thousands of men, women and children. In addition they created a host of other supply and ancillary industries, requiring a considerable labour force.

L.J. Bullen
Camborne, Cornwall
January, 2004

one

South Crofty Mine

The era of South Crofty portrayed in the following photographs embraces approximately 100 years. The former Cost Book Company was converted into a limited liability company in 1906. It was the last metalliferous mine at work in Cornwall when operations ceased in 1998. Volume One of *Mining in Cornwall* also has a section devoted to South Crofty.

Left: Palmer's shaft, *c.* 1900. A group of miners stand at the shaft collar, waiting to go underground at the commencement of a shift. It will be noted that the skip is out of the shaft guides to allow the gig (or cage) to be used for man riding at change of shift.

Below: Palmer's shaft, *c.* 1907. The house contained a 60in pumping engine. On the extreme left is the mine Counthouse, which is still recognisable today. The concrete loadings streaked with grease once held the flywheel, drum and crank of the previous horizontal winding engine. At the time this photograph was taken, a new and more modern winder had just been installed. (See Volume One). The riveted tube is an early type of air receiver. Note the two pipes leading to the shaft which carried the compressed air underground for the use of rock drills.

Palmer's shaft, 28 February 1910. This picture was taken at the 170-fathom level. A 'machine man' and his mate are using a Stephens rock drill. Note the candle stuck to the vertical stretcher bar with a lump of clay. (Photo: J.C. Burrow FRPS)

Robinson's shaft, *c.* 1904. A view looking north taken from the bob platform of the 80in pumping engine. This shows, from left to right, the Fraser & Chalmers air compressor and Holman-built steam winding engine being erected. Two of the eventual three Lancashire boilers are in place. One of the boomstays of the wooden headgear is on the left, with temporary cleats for climbing as it was still being constructed.

Robinson's shaft, c. 1912, taken from the west. On the extreme left of the picture can dimly be seen the winding engine on Engine shaft of East Pool Mine. The steel stack of the winding and compressor engines was later replaced with a stone and brick structure. The headgear left of centre is on Palmer's shaft and was a new one erected when the pumping engine house at that shaft was demolished. In the right background is the 90in pumping engine house on Highburrow East shaft of the Carn Brea Mines.

Robinson's shaft, c. 1912. Taken from the north-east and showing from left to right the boiler house roofs, winder and compressor houses with their respective exhaust pipes, the 80in pumping engine house, headgear and crusher station, the miners' dry (change house), sawmill and weighbridge house. A line of wagons drawn by a horse is on its way to the Mill in the Tuckingmill valley. Note the typical round Cornish magazine (explosives store) with the lightning conductor. Over the dry can be seen the top of the headgear of Martin's East shaft at the Tincroft Mine.

Right: Robinson's shaft, *c.* 1922; taken at the time when the mine was flooded to half of its depth. This situation was caused by the prevailing low price of tin and the flooding of East Pool & Agar Mines after the disastrous run of ground which destroyed their Engine shaft and Mitchell's shaft. It will be noted that a large number of underground wagons have been brought to surface.

Below: Robinson's shaft from the south-west, 1920s. The sawmill, fitting shop, carpenters shop and blacksmiths shop are on the left. The dark building with the short stack is the miners' dry and the left-hand stack serves the boilers of the winding engine and air compressor. The tall wooden headgear, crusher station and finally the 80in pumping engine house complete the scene.

Overleaf: East shaft, *c.* 1908. The late Captain John Thomas was exploring the old stopes of the New Cookskitchen Mine and discovered high copper, wolfram and arsenic values plus payable values of tin. This view shows the early stages of the work to recommence mining through East shaft, utilising a small steam hoist, headgear and spalling (breaking rock with sledgehammers) shed. Horses and carts are conveying the ore to the mill. Robinson's shaft is in the right background.

East shaft, a later stage in the development of this shaft, showing a new headgear and ore bins that have been erected. The long set of trestles carrying the endless rope wagon haulage to the crusher station at New Cookskitchen shaft can be seen disappearing into the distance. The trestle structure in the foreground was being built to carry the driving gear for this haulage.

New Cookskitchen shaft, *c.* 1909. The shaft collar is visible to the right of the tall crusher station building. When this shaft had only been sunk a short distance, a drop in the price of tin caused the work to be suspended. It was then decided to use the horizontal steam-winding engine to hoist from East shaft. The pulley stands carrying the rope to East shaft can be clearly seen. The trestle on the left is at the other end of the scene depicted in the previous photograph. Eventually, the sinking of New Cookskitchen shaft was restarted and this winder returned to its original function. East shaft was then equipped with its own horizontal steam winder, which appears in a photograph later in this volume. One of South Crofty's calciner stacks is on the left and, in the background on the right, is the tall stack of the Urban Electric Supply Co.'s generating station at the top of East Hill, Tuckingmill.

Bickford's shaft, *c.* 1909. Around this time the decision was made to reopen this shaft. It was equipped with a geared horizontal steam winder, which had been purchased from Dolcoath Mine some years earlier where it had been employed in the initial sinking of the Williams shaft. South Crofty used it in the sinking of Robinson's shaft and later it was re-erected at Bickford's. This view shows the crusher station, ore bins and the tramway that conveyed the ore to the mill. (Photo: J.C. Burrow FRPS)

Palmer's and Bickford's shafts, *c.* 1909. Both shafts have been re-equipped with new headgears and replacement steam-winding engines. With the removal of the pumping engine on Palmer's shaft it had been intended to strip out the pitwork and put in a double skip road, hence the two sheave wheels in that headgear. As it turned out the second wheel was only used to winch out the pitwork, and some of the bottom pitwork remained in the shaft until operations ceased. It will be noted that a low gantry has been erected between Palmer's and the Bickford's crusher, thus enabling ore from both shafts to be crushed at Bickford's.

Above: Bickford's shaft, *c.* 1930. An electrically driven three-throw ram pump at the 140-fathom level.

Left: New Cookskitchen shaft, *c.* 1912. The permanent headgear being erected at the time the shaft sinking was restarted. Work had been suspended some years before, but the mine's financial situation had improved, thus allowing operations to continue.

New Cookskitchen shaft, *c.* 1913. A view looking down the shaft when it was sinking at about the 148-fathom level. This shaft, measuring 18ft x 6ft within timbers, is divided into four compartments. It eventually reached a depth of 380 fathoms. (Photo: J.C. Burrow FRPS)

New Cookskitchen shaft, 1920s. The 90in pumping engine and boiler house, which contained three Lancashire boilers, taken only a year or so after the plant had been installed. Note the horse and cart delivering coal.

New Cookskitchen shaft, 1920s. Left to right: the crusher station which dealt with ore from this shaft and East shaft (via the trestle leading off right of the picture), the headgear and the house containing the 90in pumping engine.

New Cookskitchen shaft, *c.* 1938. A Lancashire boiler, which was purchased from Wheal Kitty at St Agnes, being delivered by a Burrell Traction Engine No.3816.

New Cookskitchen shaft, *c.* 1945. A Lancashire boiler being offloaded. This was to be installed as an additional boiler for the 90in pumping engine, bringing the total to four boilers. Pickford's tractor had hauled this boiler from Newcastle.

New Cookskitchen shaft, *c.* 1945. The boiler seen in the previous print is in place and the boiler house walls are being built around it.

New Cookskitchen shaft, 1940s. This shows the gearwork of the 90in pumping engine. The driver is the late Billy House, who had driven the engine when it was at the Fortescue's shaft of the Grenville United Mines. South Crofty purchased the engine and re-erected it on this shaft in 1922. Billy House was one of the three drivers until his retirement in the late 1940s.

New Cookskitchen shaft, *c.* 1948. This picture shows the middle chamber of the 90in pumping engine. Just after the Second World War, the engine had been fitted with a mechanical lubricator the delivery pipes of which are clearly visible. (Photo: W.J. Bassett-Lowke)

Above: New Cookskitchen shaft, 1940s. The late Joe Angove, one of the three drivers of the 90in pumping engine. He is standing on the bob platform looking at the bob and, ironically, this was the side of the beam that broke in December, 1950. Joe Angove drove this engine at the Grenville United Mines, as did Billy House. (G.W.F. Ellis)

Opposite below: The Californian stamps, *c.* 1910. This is the motor house showing the electric motors that drove the sixty head of stamps. (Photo: J.C. Burrow FRPS)

Above: New Cookskitchen shaft, 1922. The beam of the 90in pumping engine which had been hauled from the Grenville United Mines by two traction engines. It is about to be pulled up the skidway and through the cylinder opening of the engine house. The man standing alone on the right is the late Archie Tonkin, whose firm of engineers had the contract to dismantle, transport and re-erect the engine, whilst the centre figure standing in the rear is the late Billy Jenkin, a man of immense experience in engine erection. On the left of the scene the man wearing a miner's helmet is the late Jack Viall, one of the underground captains at South Crofty.

Above: New Cookskitchen shaft, *c.* 1949. This was taken from the trackbed of the former G.W.R. North Crofty branch line, and is a general view showing the pumping engine house, headgear and crusher station. Nearer the camera is the roof of the steam winder house, followed by the boiler house, stack and compressor house. The trestle, nearly buried in dump material, carries the tramway from the crusher station to the mill.

Right: New Cookskitchen shaft, 1937. The wooden headgear is being replaced by a steel one. The new taller headgear is almost complete whilst the original structure is still in service.

Opposite above: The arsenic refinery, 1940s. A man is shovelling crude arsenic, prior to its going into the refining furnace where it will be burnt to produce the snow-white pure arsenic. Arsenic was a by-product of the tin processing which, prior to the discovery of modern insecticides, pesticides etc., was a saleable commodity. (Photo: G.W.F. Ellis)

Opposite below: Sample House, 1940s. Captain Tom Davey, (Surface boss) with a vanning shovel, on which a very rich tin sample has been 'thrown up'. This is being carefully deposited in crucibles for roasting to drive off the sulphides.

New Cookskitchen shaft, *c.* 1938. One side (or web) of an additional balance box is being raised by the steam capstan into the headgear prior to lowering into the shaft. This bob had been the surface balance box at Straypark shaft of Dolcoath Mine. Note that the new steel headgear is in use but the old wooden one has not yet been fully dismantled. This was the last balance box to be taken underground in Cornwall.

New Cookskitchen shaft, *c.* 1938. The side of the balance bob is now standing in the headgear and will shortly be lowered into the shaft.

New Cookskitchen shaft, late 1930s. Two 20in columns (rising Main) bolted together and being hoisted by the capstan prior to lowering into the shaft.

SOUTH CROFTY MINE.

Opposite above: New Cookskitchen shaft, early 1920s. A group of men standing outside the materials store. Left to right: one of the winding engine drivers, 'Toshy' Luke, foreman timberman, and Joe Pascoe.

Opposite below: New Cookskitchen shaft, *c.* 1923. A general view of the shaft buildings, etc. taken from the gantry that carried the tramway from East shaft to the crusher station.

Right: Robinson's shaft, 1930s. A shaft station showing two men pushing loaded wagons into the double-decked cage. (Photo: Edgar Brooke)

Below: Robinson's shaft, late 1920s. Left to right: the end of the dry, crusher station, ore bins, headgear and the 80in pumping engine house.

Robinson's shaft, *c.* 1949. The last pole case (part of a plunger pole lift in Cornish pitwork) to be fabricated at South Crofty. The right-hand figure is the late Wilfred Stevens, foreman fitter, and next to him is the late Bill Harvey, senior pitman. The ore bins and chutes are in the background, and also the cab of one of the diesel locomotives that worked the tramway from here to the mill.

Robinson's shaft, late 1940s. The men are stocking a pole. A cast-iron plunger pole (which fits into the pole case in the previous photograph) is being 'stocked' with timber. The team of men are using a battering ram suspended on the tripod to drive the timber into the cast-iron pole. The furthest building is the electricity substation and the nearest building the electric compressor house.

Robinson's shaft, late 1940s. The man is wedging a pole, which is the second and final operation following the stocking described earlier. The sharpened pick hilts, cut about 2-3ft in length, are driven in with a sledgehammer to completely ensure that the cast iron case is watertight.

Above: The mine yard in front of the Counthouse in Station Road, Pool. The great majority of the workforce of the mine went on strike early in 1939. This scene shows the men waiting to pick up their last pay packets – in fact, the strike had already commenced when this photograph was taken. The separate small groups in the foreground are those who decided not to strike, whereas the many men in the background are the strikers.

Left: Robinson's shaft, *c.* 1930, a view from the north-west. Left to right: the stack which served the boilers of the winding and compressor engines, electricity substation, electric compressor house, pumping engine house, headgear, crusher station and ore bins. In the foreground is the magazine, seen in an earlier photograph, which has now acquired a 'blast wall' surrounding it.

Robinson's shaft, 1950s, a general view from the south-west. It will be noted that the short stack of the dry is lightly smoking. In the field in the foreground a former 'Coco pan' side tipping wagon has been partially sunk into the ground to serve as a water trough for cattle!

Robinson's shaft, early 1950s. A Lancashire boiler is being delivered by Pickfords. The vehicle is standing in the coal yard, which later became a car park at the demise of steam power.

Above: Robinson's shaft, 1940s. Back stoping. After the main level had been driven, a number of boxholes were put up from that level at about 25ft centres and an intermediate (or sub) level driven along which connected the tops of the boxholes. The stoping of the back would then commence. The central figure is Jimmy 'Jimmer' Rowe, who is about to start stoping. (Photo: G.W.F. Ellis)

Opposite above: Robinson's shaft, 1940s. This is the 310-fathom station, and the right-hand figure is the late Joe Toy, foreman timberman. (Photo: G.W.F. Ellis)

Opposite below: Robinson's shaft, 1940s. 'Croust' time at the 290-fathom level. (Photo: G.W.F. Ellis)

Above: Robinson's shaft, 1940s. Another scene at 'croust time', showing a shaft station and the cagemen enjoying their break.

Left: Robinson's shaft, 1940s. The gearwork of the 80in pumping engine, which worked on this shaft for over fifty years.

Opposite below: Robinson's shaft, *c.* 1940. A further view of the well-work from Killifreth Mine.

Robinson's shaft, *c.* 1940. This shows the parts of the condenser of the Killifreth Mine 85in pumping engine. At this time the 85in engines at Killifreth and Wheal Busy were standing idle and about to be scrapped to provide metal for the war effort. South Crofty was fully aware of the enormous problems that could be caused by enemy action resulting in damage to either of their own two pumping engines. With this in mind, they purchased the Wheal Busy engine. However, the well-work (condenser) of this engine had been badly corroded by the acid water of that mine, whereas the condensing work of the Killifreth engine was in good order and capable of being adapted for use with the Wheal Busy engine. Consequently, this was purchased prior to the scrapping of the Killifreth engine. The figure is the late J.H. Trounson. Note in the background the improvised air-raid shelter as a lean to at the end of the ore bin!

Robinson's shaft, 1930s. A Cornish boiler is being offloaded. The building on the left is the boiler house for the winding and compressor engines.

New Cookskitchen shaft, 1940s. The balance box at the 205-fathom level. The figure on the right is the late J.H. Trounson. (Photo: Edgar Brooke)

Right: New Cookskitchen shaft, 1940s. At the 195-fathom level, showing a 20in pole of the pitwork of the pumping engine. This was one of the largest plunger poles ever used in the county. The figure is the late Edgar Brooke.

Below: East shaft, *c.* 1921. Reference is made earlier in this book to this shaft being equipped with its own winding engine subsequent to the re-commencement of the sinking of New Cookskitchen shaft, seen in the background. This scene shows the final arrangement at East shaft with a horizontal steam-winding engine.

Above: Robinson's shaft, 1964. The Holman-built, horizontal steam-winding engine. This was a very fast engine capable of hoisting at speeds in excess of 2,000ft per minute. The cylinders were 22ins in diameter and the stroke was 48ins, whilst the winding drums were 8ft in diameter. In this scene the driver is marking his fine control positions on the circumference of the right-hand drum and his fireman is oiling up just prior to commencing a shift winding ore from over 2,000ft underground. The driver is the late Charlie Buzza and the fireman is the late Bill Holloway – they were brothers-in-law! (Photo: W. Trengove)

Opposite above: Robinson's shaft, 1940s. This Fraser & Chalmers compound compressor was housed in the same building as the Holman horizontal winding engine. The right-hand disc of the winder can just be discerned on the left of the print.

Opposite below: Robinson's shaft, 1940s. This is at the 310-fathom level on No.2 lode. The figure on the left is Captain Arthur Stevens. (Photo: G.W.F. Ellis)

Opposite above: North Roskear Mine, Pressure shaft, late 1940s. The figure is the late N.K. Kitto, then chief surveyor and later manager of South Crofty Mine.

Left: Taken at Robinson's shaft in the late 1940s and showing the portable plant which was used in adit refurbishment and other operations over a number of years. The figure on the left is the late Charlie Francis, outside foreman, and the man standing by the boiler is the late Wilfred Stevens, foreman fitter.

Below: North Roskear Mine, Pressure shaft, late 1940s, showing the commencement of operations at this site in connection with adit refurbishment – using the portable winding plant shown in the previous photograph which is housed in the shed on the right. The three hundredweight capacity wagon is being pushed to dump.

North Roskear Mine, Pressure shaft, late 1940s. A further view of the portable plant erected and in operation.

Left: Robinson's shaft, late 1940s. Formerly, this tramway between Robinson's and the mill was horse-worked. At one time it extended even further eastwards to serve Palmer's and Bickford's shafts when they were in operation. After the Second World War it was decided to introduce diesel locomotives. Here we see a train leaving the ore bins in the background en route to the mill.

A mineral train being shunted near the bridge over Dudnance Lane. From here the wagons were hand pushed over a long trestle to the South Crofty mill.

The South Crofty Traction Engine pulling a long pump rod out of the pond in which they were stored. This engine was purchased in 1951 from Craddock's in East Cornwall for £30! The tramway in the foreground carried the trains from Robinson's shaft to the mill. In the background is the Climax Engineering Works.

New Cookskitchen shaft, spring 1942. King George VI and Queen Elizabeth visited the mine at this time and this scene shows them meeting a group of miners. The figure to the left of the king is the late N.K. Kitto, then chief surveyor at the mine.

Above: New Cookskitchen shaft, spring 1942. This picture shows Their Majesties walking past the 90in pumping engine house. The man in the trilby hat on the right is the late Josiah Paul, retired manager, and the man on the extreme right is his son, the late Clarence Paul, the then manager. Prior to coming to South Crofty, the Royal party visited the engineering works of Holman Brothers in Camborne. The queen was presented with a brooch in the form of a Holman trademark 'H', which she is wearing in her lapel.

Above: The King and Queen visited the mill and are shown here with the late Josiah Paul and his son the late Clarence Paul walking to New Cookskitchen shaft.

Right: Robinson's shaft, *c.* 1966. In 1964 work commenced on replacing the steam winder, installed in 1907, with an electric hoist. This view taken from the bob loft of the pumping engine shows the new building under construction and the drums of the electric hoist in place. At this time the steam hoist was still at work and remained in service until 1967.

Opposite below: New Cookskitchen shaft, spring 1942. This was taken from the bob loft of the pumping engine house. The Royal party is passing the compressor house, boiler house, capstan and winding engine houses. This photograph is also of interest as it shows in the background the roofs of five Brunton calciners.

Opposite page:

Above: The Counthouse, 1950s. This view shows a part of the mine model which was constructed to a scale of 1:500. The left-hand vertical rod represents Robinson's shaft, next is New Cookskitchen shaft, and on the right the New Dolcoath shaft at Roskear. The model was under construction at this stage with the various levels and workings being incorporated.

Below: New Cookskitchen shaft, 1951. Following the breakage of the beam of the 90in pumping engine in December 1950, the engineering firm of Sulzers managed to provide at short notice small high-speed centrifugal pumps and suitable motors. This prompt action, together with other emergency measures, prevented a more serious flooding of the mine.

This page:

Above: Robinson's shaft. 1951. After the accident which wrecked the 90in pumping engine at New Cookskitchen shaft in December 1950, all possible means were employed to contain the rising water throughout the mine. Here we see the use of bailing skips at Robinson's. These discharged the water at surface through a spring valve into the sliding launder, operated by the two men. The low concrete block walls were to contain and direct the water as it gushed out of the bottom of the skips.

Below: New Cookskitchen shaft, early 1950s. This was taken from the bob platform of the pumping engine after its beam had broken. It shows the surface balance box being broken up by blasting. The chalked writing 'Pigs Good Old Pal' refers to the pitman at New Cooks who rejoiced in the nickname of 'Joe Pigs'!

New Cookskitchen shaft, 1951. This is the part of the broken beam of the 90in pumping engine, weighing 7 tons, which fell across the mouth of the shaft in late December 1950. It was extremely fortunate that it did not go into the shaft as the damage would have been extensive. Here we see it in the mine yard being examined by Ernie Richards, mill manager, and Bill Harvey, senior pitman.

New Cookskitchen shaft, early 1950s. Here we see the scrapping of the pumping engine, showing the bottom of the cylinder. At the lower part of the picture can be seen the branch where the jacket steam entered the steam case.

Robinson's shaft, 1940s. A scene showing blacksmiths and fitters socketing winding ropes. There were two double-decked cages in this shaft. Under mining regulations, the chains, ropes, shackles and other fittings have to be examined regularly.

Palmer's/Bickford's shafts. In the early 1950s, when it was once again found necessary to get underground through Palmer's shaft, arrangements for re-equipping had to be considered. The winding engine on Palmer's shaft was in a very rusty condition after some thirty years out of use. However, Bickford's winder was in better fettle and its boiler was tested and found alright for use. This photograph shows the turnwheel and frame fabricated by Bartle's foundry that turned the winding rope from Bickford's winder to haul on Palmer's shaft.

Above: Palmer's/Bickford's shafts, early 1950s. A new headgear has been erected on Palmer's shaft and the new winding rope is being wound on to the drum of the Bickford's winding engine. This new rope is being wound off the manufacturer's delivery drum, out of camera shot to the left. Note that the turnwheel mentioned in the last caption can be seen to the left of the stack.

Left: Palmer's shaft, 1950s. The new stack, built at this time for Bickford's winder, is smoking and the new headgear on Palmer's shaft is seen with a gig (cage) specially constructed for this crooked shaft.

Opposite below: New Cookskitchen shaft, 1950s. The water settling sumps at the 340-fathom pump station. These were necessary in order to separate the worst of the grit from the water before being drawn in by the electric pumps.

Above: New Cookskitchen shaft, 1950s. Showing the three Sulzer pumps working in the new pump station at the 340-fathom level. These were installed following the breaking of the beam of the Cornish pumping engine and lifted the water to the 195-fathom pump station.

Above: New Cookskitchen shaft, late 1960s. Erecting a new 140ft-high steel headgear. On the right a building to contain the new electric hoist is under construction.

Opposite above: New Cookskitchen shaft, 1950s. Taken at the 340-fathom pump station, showing another area of the water settling sumps.

Opposite below: The mill, 1960s. In the background is New Cookskitchen shaft and the gantry carrying the tramway to the mill can be seen sweeping to the right. The gantry in the foreground is carrying the tramway from Robinson's shaft to the mill.

Above: New Cookskitchen shaft, late 1960s. The large former colliery winder being erected.

Opposite: New Cookskitchen shaft, late 1960s, showing the new lofty headgear near completion. At the time of writing it still stands and is the highest headgear ever erected in Cornwall. The 16ft-diameter sheave wheels are being lifted into place. Note the man standing on the sheave platform.

New Cookskitchen shaft, 1970. One of the two new six-ton capacity alloy skips for use with the new winder and headgear.

The new mill, 1970. The Californian stamps is on the left and the early stages of the erection of steelwork for a new mill is in hand. Coarse ore silos and a conveyor belt are being constructed. The new winder and headgear are fully commissioned.

Robinson's shaft, 9 June 1970. The visit of HRH the Prince of Wales, Duke of Cornwall. The scene shows the mine manager, G.C. Pengilly, explaining to the Prince a diagrammatic model of the mine prior to their descent of Robinson's shaft.

New Cookskitchen shaft, 1980s. This is a view of the sub-incline shaft which was commenced at the 380-fathom level, the bottom of the vertical shaft.

Above: The Tuckingmill decline, 1985. This decline was intended to be sunk from surface to connect with the deep workings of the mine. However, after it was sunk only for a short distance, operations ceased. The ownership of the mine had changed and a different policy of development did not include the decline. On the left is the mill and New Cookskitchen shaft.

Opposite above: New Cookskitchen and Robinson's shafts from the east, 1995. The tiered concrete block/brick stack in the foreground served the Bickford's shaft winder, which hauled on Palmer's shaft for a number of years in the 1940s and '50s.

Opposite below: New Dolcoath Mine, Roskear shaft, taken from the west in 2001. In the early 1990s South Crofty Mine decided to transfer their second egress from Robinson's shaft to this shaft. A new headgear was constructed, a winder installed and the shaft was deepened. The plant remained in use until South Crofty closed.

New Dolcoath Mine, Roskear shaft, 2001. This further view from the north shows the headgear described in the previous photograph. The brick stack in the background served the boilers of the winding engine, compressor and capstan when this 16ft-diameter brick-lined shaft was sunk to a depth of 2,000ft in the 1920s. On the left is the stone-built abutment which had supported one end of the bridge, carrying the tramway between the shaft and the crusher station over the road.

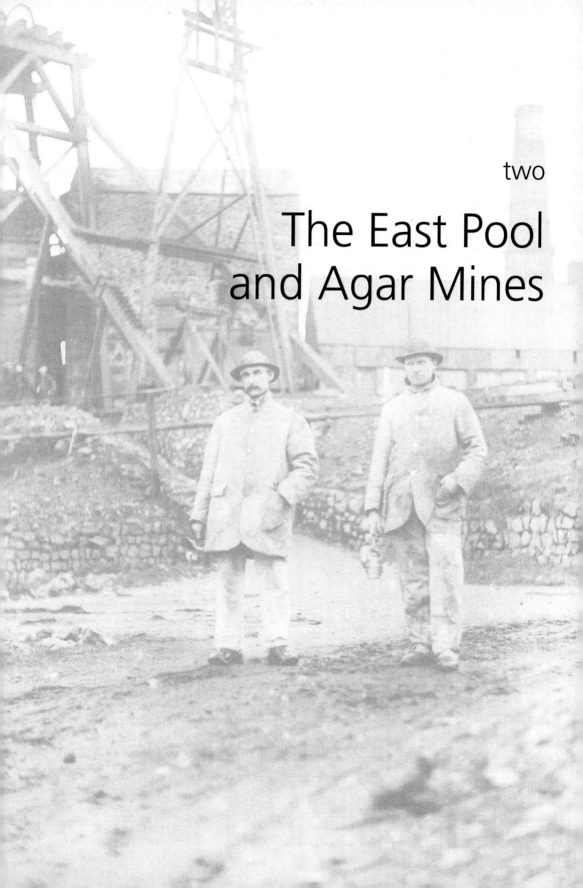

two

The East Pool and Agar Mines

The mines of East Pool and Wheal Agar were two separate companies for many years. In 1897 they were amalgamated but still as a cost book company under the title of East Pool & Agar United. Although occupying adjoining setts, they enjoyed vastly different fortunes. East Pool was one of the most successful mines ever to be wrought in Cornwall whilst Wheal Agar had a very chequered history. Most of the scenes in this pictorial review were taken in the period when the mines were being managed as a single undertaking and, from 1912 until finally closing in 1945, as a limited liability company. In Volume One of this series there are a number of photographs of these mines which complement the prints shown here.

Above: East Pool & Agar Ltd, *c.* 1912. The 212-fathom level, showing 'machine men' at work. (Photo: J.C. Burrow FRPS)

Opposite above: East Pool & Agar United Mining Co., Mitchell's and Engine shafts, *c.* 1900, showing a general view from the south. From left to right: Mitchell's shaft, crusher station and Engine shaft. The engine house contained a 70in pumping engine. Exhaust steam is coming from a small engine in the lean-to building, which drove the machine tools in the fitting shop.

Opposite below: East Pool & Agar Ltd, *c.* 1916. In the background is Mitchell's (or North) shaft winding engine. The trestle is part of a narrow gauge tramway which had been built between the mine and Carn Brea railway yard to deliver coal. Actually the stocks shown here are of anthracite, as Welsh steam coal was unobtainable during the First World War. Anthracite produces a very hot flame and caused problems with the boilers. To add to the woes, one part of these huge piles caught alight by spontaneous combustion which took the fire brigade some time to get under control!

Overleaf: The 212-fathom level showing hand hammer drills in use. (Photo: J.C. Burrow FRPS)

East Pool & Agar Ltd, *c.* 1920. Driving the 252-fathom level crosscut north to intersect the Rogers lode.

Above: East Pool & Agar Ltd, *c.* 1915, taken outside the Counthouse. Back row, left to right: Dick Gilbert, shift boss; Tom Grose, shift boss; Captain Timmins, underground manager; M.T. Taylor, mine superintendent; Willard Kemp, mine captain; Percy Maynard, purser; -?-; Jimmy Lobb, mine captain. Front row, left to right: -?-; 'Cookie' Angwin, engineer; -?-.

Opposite: East Pool & Agar Ltd, *c.* 1920. Drilling an 'upper' using a Holman 'S' model machine. (Photo: Lawley Bros)

Holman Brothers Ltd, Camborne, 1910. The No.1 works erecting shop, showing an early type of electrically driven air compressor which was made for Wheal Grenville. When that mine closed in 1921 it was purchased by East Pool & Agar Ltd and installed at their new Taylor's shaft. See also a later photograph in this volume. (Photo: J.C. Burrow FRPS)

East Pool & Agar Ltd, Engine shaft, c. 1916. A group of men at a shaft station, the man on the extreme right being Jimmy Lobb, then a shift boss. The men are standing by the auxiliary cage, which was installed in the pump compartment of the shaft after the Cornish pitwork was removed in favour of electric pumps.

East Pool & Agar Ltd, *c.* 1920, showing a group of mine captains and engineers. Left to right: Tom Grose, mine captain; Willard Kemp, mine captain; –?–; D.D. Belcham, engineer.

East Pool & Agar United Mining Co., *c.* 1911. A Holman-built electrically driven air compressor, which stood near Engine shaft.

East Pool & Agar United Mining Co., Engine shaft. Another view of the electrically driven air compressor.

East Pool & Agar Ltd., taken outside the Counthouse, c. 1925. Back row, left to right: Billy Richards, chief surveyor; –?–; –?–; Willard Kemp underground boss; Tom Grose, underground boss; D.D. Belcham, electrical engineer; Dick Gilbert, mine captain; –?–; Jimmy Lobb, foreman timberman. Seated, left to right: 'Cookie' Angwin, chief engineer; Percy Maynard, purser; M.T. Taylor, mine superintendent; Captain Timmins, underground manager.

East Pool & Agar Ltd, late 1920s. Hand drilling and possibly the last commercial hand-labour work (as opposed to drilling with rock drills powered by compressed air) to be done in Cornwall. The figure on the right is Joe Small.

Tolvaddon stamps, the site of the East Pool Mining Company's dressing floors, in the mid-1890s. This is the southernmost of the two stamps engines and in the foreground white arsenic is being removed from the labyrinth on the right. The Mines Inspectorate of today would be appalled!

Above: East Pool & Agar United Mining Co., Engine shaft, late nineteenth century. The figures are Willard Kemp, mine captain and a shift boss. The complex around Engine shaft forms the background.

Opposite below: East Pool & Agar Ltd, *c.* 1920. This shows the Counthouse and part of the mine yard. The single-storey building on the left was occupied by the weighbridge clerk. Over the roof of this building can be seen the stack and house of Engine shaft winder. Further right is another stack that took some of the flues from the winding engine and compressor boilers. Behind the Counthouse is a large chimney, which had been built during the First World War for a bank of boilers that were never commissioned because of the collapse of Engine shaft in 1921.

East Pool & Agar Ltd, Mitchell's shaft, *c.* 1920, showing the headgear, landing brace and tramway trestle to the crusher station. The now preserved beam winding engine at Pool hoisted from this shaft. In the bottom right can be seen the rails of the Camborne & Redruth tramway spur which served the ore bins.

East Pool & Agar Ltd, Engine shaft, *c.* 1913. On the extreme left of the print is the stack of Waddington's shaft pumping engine at Wheal Agar. The building to the right is the crusher station, and further right is the headgear on Engine shaft. It will be noted that the 70in pumping engine on this shaft has been dismantled, having been replaced by electric pumps. The derelict building housed Old Tiger Whim, scrapped long before, and the white building was the miners' dry.

Right: East Pool and Agar Ltd, Engine shaft, 1920. These were the last two miners to come up from underground when work was suspended at the commencement of the great slump.

Below: Tolvaddon stamps, *c.* 1900, taken from the bob platform of the South stamps engine and showing the extensive treatment plant below the stamps. The derelict pumping engine house across the valley is on Tregonning's shaft of Wheal Seton, which had contained a 70in engine. The extensive dumps on the skyline over this building are those of Tilly's Engine shaft, the principal shaft of Wheal Seton. On the left skyline is Holman's No.2 Works, more commonly known as Boiler Works.

Tolvaddon stamps, late nineteenth century. On the left is the South stamps engine house, with the stack of the North stamps engine just showing over the roof. In the foreground the tall left-hand stack served the calciner flues of East Pool, whilst the right-hand stack served the many tin stream burning houses in this part of the Red river valley.

Tolvaddon in the late nineteenth century. Showing the two sets of Cornish stamps and the extensive dressing floors of East Pool Mine. Nearer to the camera are independent tin stream works.

Tolvaddon stamps, early 1920s. The building with skylights housed the Holman pneumatic stamps. The South Cornish stamps engine, then disused, is to the right, whilst the long trestle carries the tramway from the mine at Illogan Highway. The iron stack served the boilers of the Holman-built horizontal engine that drove the new stamps.

East Pool & Agar Ltd, *c.* 1911. Left to right: Steam compressor house, the pumping engine stack, and house and headgear on Engine shaft. The long gantry is leading to the crusher station, with a further gantry extending from the crushers to the headgear on Mitchell's shaft. Mitchell's winding engine and Pool Methodist church are in the background. Between the crusher station and Mitchell's shaft is the Pitman's house. This photograph was taken from the burrows of Wheal Agar, and the Camborne–Redruth road runs through the middle of the scene – note the tramway poles.

The Camborne & Redruth Tramway, *c.* 1904. An unusual feature of this public tramway system was the use of mineral trains that, for part of their journey, ran on the public highway. This shows the brakesman operating the points to allow a train to enter the crusher siding which served two shafts of the East Pool & Agar United Mining Co.

The Camborne & Redruth Tramway, *c.* 1910. A snowy day with a public service tram being followed by a mineral train in the village of Pool, where the Methodist church is still recognisable today. On the left is a Bal maiden.

East Pool & Agar Ltd, *c.* 1912. This was taken from the bank by Engine shaft and shows the beam winder with the housing covering the winding drums. Because the deep Engine (or South) shaft was vertical, this winder, unlike most others of its type which hauled on crooked compound shafts, was able to attain a considerable turn of speed. It is clearly a cold winter's day as the pond water, having been pumped from underground, is steaming. The engine house on the right once contained a winder known as 'Old Tiger Whim' and the building in the rear is the miners' dry. In the left background can be seen Willoughby's shaft headgear, the top of Martin's East shaft headgear, and stacks all at North Tincroft Mine. On the hillside showing dimly is the tall lattice steel headgear on the Williams shaft of Dolcoath Mine.

Above: East Pool Mining Co., 1890s. This photograph was taken from the rear of the Pool Methodist church. Left to right: Engine shaft headgear, 70in pumping engine house, fitting shop, derelict house of 'Old Tiger Whim', miners' dry, Engine shaft winder, main blacksmith's shop, the Counthouse and the small white building is the weighbridge office.

Left: East Pool & Agar Ltd, 1930s. Engine shaft beam winder, which had been out of use since 1921.

Opposite below: East Pool & Agar Ltd, Engine shaft, 1930s. A further view of the derelict winder showing the new drums which had been fabricated by Holman Bros. of Camborne, one of which could be clutched out. In the event the new arrangement for clutching was never used.

Above: East Pool and Agar Ltd, 1930s. Engine shaft beam winder, which by this time had fallen into a very derelict condition. The stack on the left, now truncated to the stonework, served a bank of boilers which steamed both the beam winding engine and the former Carn Brea Mine compressor and horizontal winder, which were later erected here. This horizontal winder operated the auxiliary cage, which was installed in the space occupied by the pitwork in the shaft after the pumping engine ceased working.

Above: East Pool & Agar Ltd, 1930s, showing the Engine shaft winder being scrapped. In the background is the winding engine on Mitchell's shaft, which has been preserved.

Left: East Pool & Agar Ltd, late 1930s, taken at the time the Engine shaft beam winder was being scrapped and showing the cylinder, cylinder cover and piston rod.

Right: East Pool & Agar Ltd, 1945. The Robartes engine shaft horizontal steam winder in a derelict condition shortly before being scrapped.

Below: East Pool & Agar Ltd, 1930s. A photograph taken from the bob platform of the Wheal Agar, Robartes shaft 90in pumping engine showing the external nose of the beam when the plant was derelict. The stack and house of the horizontal winding engine are in the background.

A view from the dressing (treatment) floors of Wheal Uny situated above Redruth Coombe facing north-west in about 1895. The stack and separate engine house in the left middle ground is the stamps engine of Wheal Agar, situated in the Tolskithy valley. When the mine amalgamated with the East Pool Mining Co. in 1897, the treatment of ore from both mines was undertaken at Tolvaddon and the Wheal Agar stamps shut down.

Wheal Agar stamps, c. 1910. This was situated in the Tolskithy valley and the house on the right once contained the rotary engine which drove the stamps. The house and its associated stack are mentioned in the previous photograph, but by this time the machinery had been removed. This site was chosen by the Cornwall Tailings Company to treat the massive tailings dumps of the Carn Brea and Tincroft Mines and their new buildings appear here.

East Pool & Agar Ltd. Robartes Engine shaft, early 1940s. This shows the doorway leading from the bottom floor of the engine house to the boiler house at the time when the site had become derelict. The wooden stairs have already disappeared. Note that the gearwork of the 90in engine can be discerned.

East Pool & Agar Ltd, Robartes Engine shaft, 1930s. It will be noted that in many of the photographs of this shaft there is only one sheave wheel in the headgear. The second wheel was removed in 1922 and used as a turn wheel to carry the rope from the Agar winder to the Taylor's shaft, thus enabling this winder to sink the new shaft.

East Pool & Agar Ltd, Robartes Engine shaft, *c.* 1944. The nose of the 90in pumping engine is in the 'indoors' position and the engine had been derelict for many years. The tall capstan shears is in the middle of the photograph. However, the solitary headgear wheel has a rope running over it once again. At this time a firm of scrap merchants were engaged in stripping out the pitwork from the shaft and they made use of the winding engine for this purpose. This was the very last time the engine worked.

East Pool & Agar Ltd, Robartes Engine shaft, 1940s. The plug door of the engine house is boarded up and one leg of the headgear is on the left with the hotwell of the engine between the two. On the right is the bottom of one of the legs of the capstan shears and the wheel that carried the rope from the steam capstan to the wheel at the top of the shears.

East Pool & Agar Ltd, Robartes Engine shaft, mid–1940s. This was taken at the time the engine was being scrapped.

East Pool & Agar Ltd, Robartes Engine shaft, mid–1940s. A view from the bob loft of this 90in pumping engine, looking down on to the cylinder cover and valve chest in the middle chamber. This scene reflects the dereliction of many years and within a short time the engine was scrapped.

Left: East Pool & Agar Ltd, Robartes Engine shaft, mid-1940s. A front view of the 90in pumping engine house at the time the engine was being scrapped. Part of the wooden headgear and capstan shears can be seen. The men standing on the bob wall give some indication of the size of the building. The figure standing by the plug door is the late J.H. Trounson.

Below: East Pool & Agar Ltd, Robartes Engine shaft, late 1940s. Showing South Crofty Mine's portable adit plant headgear being erected to give access underground to construct a dam at the 48-fathom level below adit. The building, still retaining its roof, was the former steam capstan house.

East Pool & Agar Ltd, Robartes Engine shaft, late 1940s. The headgear referred to in the previous scene has been erected. The third figure from the right is the late Bill Harvey, senior shaftman.

Carn Brea Mine, Highburrow East shaft, c. 1916. A snowy scene with the pumping engine stack smoking. The mine had closed in 1913 but a consortium of neighbouring mines agreed to keep this engine working to prevent the rising waters in Carn Brea from affecting them. A little later this 90in pumping engine was purchased by East Pool & Agar Ltd and re-erected on their new Taylor's shaft. The headgear to the right is on Old Sump shaft of Carn Brea Mine.

Tolgus Mines Ltd, May 1923. This venture was undertaken by an associated company of East Pool & Agar Ltd, which was formed to sink a new shaft in the Tolgus concession. It was intended to seek the continuation of a lode discovered before the shaft collapsed at East Pool in 1921. The scene shows Captain Algernon H. Moreing, MP, cutting the first sod of the new shaft. The lady with a speckled straw hat immediately behind Captain Moreing was an aunt to the author.

Tolgus Mines Ltd, May 1923. A photograph taken immediately after the previous scene, showing the men digging up the turf following the formal ceremony. The man now holding the shining spade is William Richards, chief surveyor of E.P. & A. Ltd; and on his left is Tom Grose, mine captain; M.T. Taylor, mine superintendent; and the tall figure in a wing collar is Mr E.A. Loring, company director. (Photo: T.E. Surbey)

Above: Tolgus Mines Ltd, 1927. This shows the sinking headgear just prior to the venture being abandoned. The steam winding engine is in the foreground, whilst the boiler house and stack are on the right.

Above: Tolgus Mines Ltd, 1927. Dismantling the plant after the mine had closed. The boom stays have been removed from the headgear and one of the two boilers has been taken out of the boiler house. Over the roof of the blacksmiths shop the East Pool Traction engine can be seen. The sinking of a 2,000ft shaft and considerable development underground had ended in total failure.

Overleaf: East Pool & Agar Ltd, Taylor's shaft, 1922. On the left is a sheerlegs, which is standing on the site of the great chimney yet to be built. The sinking headgear clearly shows the unusual arrangement of the winding rope being carried under a turn wheel in the boomstays and then horizontally for some 900ft to the south in order to make use of the Wheal Agar (Robartes) winder for sinking this new shaft.

Left: East Pool & Agar
Ltd, Taylor's shaft, 1922.
The 110ft stack is nearly
completed and it was to
serve the boilers of both
the pumping and winding
engines.

Below: East Pool & Agar
Ltd, Taylor's shaft, *c.* 1922.
This was taken from the east,
showing the sinking headgear
with the sinking kibble
visible. The permanent
winding engine, which had
been purchased from the
closed Botallack mine, is
being erected and the first
of the Lancashire boilers for
the winder has been placed.
The masons are at work on
the stack. On the skyline
left of centre is the stack
and cooling tower of the
electricity works at the top of
East Hill.

Right: East Pool & Agar Ltd, Taylor's shaft in 1923, showing the hoisting of the permanent headgear whilst the 110ft stack is now completed. The commencement of this shaft was not attended with any official ceremony. However, a number of interested persons came to see the shaft template when about a foot of soil had been removed. Among them was the author's late father and eldest brother (then a boy of five) who was lifted into and out of the shallow excavation and then told 'you have been to the bottom of Taylor's shaft'!

Below: East Pool & Agar Ltd, Taylor's shaft, 1923. The stack and permanent winding engine house are complete whilst the air compressor house is under construction and the permanent headgear is erected. The building right of centre with roof timbers in place is the carpenter's shop. This had been brought from the closed Wheal Grenville where it had housed an air compressor also acquired by the company for this shaft. The drill sharpening shop is the small building with a chimney. On the left is the site office and the figure is the late M.T. Taylor, mine superintendent.

East Pool & Agar Ltd, Taylor's shaft, 1923. A view from the north-west, when the house for the 90in pumping engine from the Carn Brea Mine was being built. In the foreground, left to right, can be seen the cylinder bottom of the engine, cylinder cover and other smaller parts.

East Pool & Agar Ltd, Taylor's shaft, 1923. A further stage in the development of the new shaft site. The sinking headgear is still in use and the pulley stands carrying the winding rope to the winder on Robarte's shaft are clearly shown. By this time the permanent headgear was erected, as were the stack, winding engine, compressor and electricity substation buildings. On the extreme right the carpenter's shop is being completed. The temporary narrow gauge tramways conveyed the waste rock from the shaft sinking to the dumps near the old Agar shafts. Between the boom stays of the headgear the Counthouse of North Pool Mine can be seen.

East Pool & Agar Ltd, Taylor's shaft, 1923. Here we see the 52-ton beam on trucks and the two traction engines which had hauled the load from Carn Brea Mine. Standing by the beam is the late Johnny Ellis, who had been in charge of the dismantling and was about to re-erect the engine in its new house.

East Pool & Agar Ltd, Taylor's shaft, 1923. This is the 52-ton cast-iron beam of the pumping engine just after it had been hauled on to the site. Note how the boiler plates which had been laid down are being distorted by the great weight.

East Pool & Agar Ltd, Taylor's shaft. 1923. Taken from the north-east and showing, from left to right, the winding engine boiler house, winding engine house, the stack which served both sets of boilers, pumping engine house and, at the side of the pumping engine house, the boiler house is being built.

East Pool & Agar Ltd, Taylor's shaft, 1923. The 52-ton beam is seen just prior to being hauled through the engine house and raised on to the bob wall. The cylinder bottom is in the foreground.

East Pool & Agar Ltd, Taylor's shaft, 1924. A general view from the south. From left to right are the ore bins, crusher station, headgear (which nearly obscures the pumping engine house), the boiler house of the pumping engine, the capstan which has yet to have its house built, winder and compressor houses. In the foreground are pitwork castings waiting to be lowered underground.

East Pool & Agar Ltd, Taylor's shaft, late 1920s. A group of miners at the shaft collar about to start a shift underground. The man on the left in a duck jacket is a mine captain.

GROUP OF CO

MINERS.

East Pool & Agar Ltd, Taylor's shaft, *c.* 1925. The mine is now in production and the new branch of the Camborne & Redruth Tramway has been laid into the ore bins. The horizontal sheave wheel and the pulley stands formed a part of the arrangement described earlier to use the Agar winding engine to sink the new shaft.

Above: East Pool & Agar Ltd, Taylor's shaft, *c.* 1930. This photograph was taken from the extensive Wheal Agar Mine burrows and provides a good overall view of the shaft complex.

Previous spread: East Pool & Agar Ltd, Taylor's shaft, late 1920s. A further group photograph taken at the same period and once again the boss is in evidence.

Above: East Pool & Agar Ltd, Taylor's shaft, 1930s. An internal view of the compressor house. The compressor on the right was built by Holman's of Camborne for the old East Pool company and re-erected here in the 1920s, whilst the left-hand engine was built for Wheal Grenville and stood at Fortescue's shaft of that mine. It was purchased when Wheal Grenville closed. On the right is one of the two small vertical compressors that had been brought over from the Tolgus Mine when that project was abandoned.

Right: East Pool & Agar Ltd, Taylor's shaft, 1934. The ore bins that were used by the electrically hauled trains to transport ore to Tolvaddon mill. Note the 3ft 6in gauge track running to both sides of the structure. The front wall of the crusher station is on the left.

Above: East Pool & Agar Ltd, Taylor's shaft, early 1930s. Taken at the 1,322ft level and showing a small kibble being hoisted from a winze using a Holman air winch. The man on the right, Harry Goldsworthy, was from Devonshire and had earlier worked at the Gawton Mine on the banks of the River Tamar.

Opposite above: East Pool & Agar Ltd, Taylor's shaft, 1930s. An underground scene showing the late J.H. Trounson on the right with a group of students from the Camborne School of Mines.

Opposite below: East Pool & Agar Ltd, Taylor's shaft, 1930s. A view of the nose of the beam of the 90in pumping engine taken from the headgear. The figure standing on the bob plat is the late J.H. Trounson.

East Pool & Agar Ltd, Taylor's shaft, early 1930s. Another scene at the top of the winze sunk below the 1,322ft level. Captain Fred Scoble is climbing into the ladder and Harry Goldsworthy is landing a kibble.

Previous spread: East Pool & Agar Ltd, Taylor's shaft, early 1930s. Captain Fred Scoble at the 1,322ft level, landing a kibble from a winze.

Right: East Pool & Agar Ltd, Taylor's shaft, 1930s. This was taken from the headgear and shows the house pole which raised the condensing water of the pumping engine to join the main water from underground to the level of the bob plat. This was necessary in order to overcome the difference in level between Taylor's shaft and Illogan Highway. From that point it followed the long established water course to Tolvaddon in order to provide dressing water.

Below: East Pool & Agar Ltd, Taylor's shaft, late 1920s. A fine view from north-west of the 110ft stack, the 90in pumping engine, headgear, crusher station and ore bins.

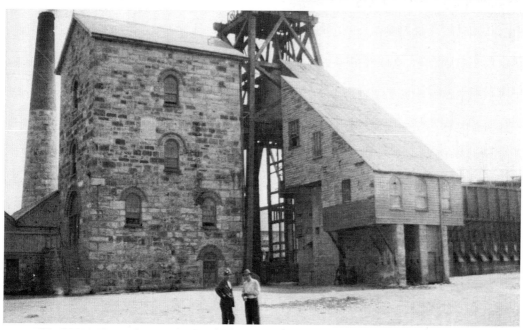

East Pool & Agar Ltd, Taylor's shaft, late 1920s. A view from the south-west, which is of interest because it shows four loaded wagons under the chutes of the ore bin awaiting collection by a locomotive. Lovelock's concrete block works, which used the waste rock from the mine to produce building blocks, is on the right.

East Pool & Agar Ltd, Taylor's shaft, 1920s. A train of empty wagons is arriving from Tolvaddon stamps to load at the ore bins.

East Pool & Agar Ltd, Taylor's shaft, *c.* 1940. A sump shaft was sunk from the 1,600ft level to the 1,900ft level. This was 1,050ft west of Taylor's shaft. It was always referred to as the electric winze and the 1,700, 1,800 and 1,900ft levels were initially developed from this shaft. From left to right: D.D. Belcham, electrical engineer; Tom Grose, underground manager; Sam Scoble, shift boss; and Fred Scoble, mine captain.

Left: Tolvaddon stamps, 1940s. A water wheel driving one of the Brunton calciners.

Below: Tolvaddon stamps, 1940s. On the right is the old North stamps engine house. In front of this is a beam, formerly connected to the old stamps engine which returned dressing water for milling. This function was still accomplished by a balance weight, as shown, and an electric motor with a crank and connecting rod at the other end.

Tolvaddon stamps, *c.* 1920. The Pneumatic stamps that replaced the two sets of Cornish stamps in 1908 were driven by a Holman-built Corliss valve compound steam engine, and the steel stack served the boilers of this engine. At a later date the stamps were powered by electricity. The stamps building is on the left and, dominating the scene, is part of a trestle carrying the tramway from the mine.

Overleaf:

Top left: Tolvaddon stamps, 1940s. The photographer is standing on the trackbed of the former mineral tramway at a point approximately where the trestle commenced. In the middle ground can be seen the remains of the trestle. This tramway was replaced by an aerial ropeway in 1934 and the turn station framework of this is clearly visible. The bridge-like safety canopy over the road is on the right.

Bottom left: Tolvaddon stamps, 1940s. The dressing floors complex and, in the foreground, a calciner stack.

Top right: Tolvaddon stamps, 1945. Showing some of the James sand tables in the treatment floors just after operations ceased.

Bottom right: Tolvaddon stamps, 1944. A good general view of the aerial ropeway and stamps buildings. The return dressing water launder, referred to in a previous photograph, can be seen on the left. In the foreground is a tramway that conveyed the tin concentrate to the calciners.

Tolvaddon stamps, 1945. Some of the battery of Holman Pneumatic stamps seen immediately after the plant had closed down.

Tolvaddon stamps, 1945. A number of kieves in which the tin concentrate was tossed by men with Cornish shovels to obtain a final upgrading. At this time the mill had just ceased production.

Above left: Tolvaddon stamps, *c.* 1931. An experimental 'in mill' tin smelting plant on test. The figures are Willie Bennett, assayer; Mr Kaiser, the inventor of the plant; and Mr Smith, a student from the Camborne School of Mines. This equipment was eventually deemed to be a failure.

Above right: Tolvaddon stamps, 1934. The construction of the steelwork at the mill for the aerial ropeway that replaced the mineral trains for conveying the ore from Taylor's shaft.

Right: East Pool & Agar Ltd. Taylor's shaft, 1934. The aerial ropeway tensioning plant photographed from the top of the new ore bin when newly commissioned. The pylons can be seen over the fields in the direction of Tolvaddon.

Above: Tolvaddon stamps, 1935. The aerial ropeway from Taylor's shaft at the mill terminal. On the right is a wall and truncated stack of the South Cornish stamps engine house, which had ceased working in 1908.

Opposite above: East Pool & Agar Ltd, Taylor's shaft, 1934. Construction of the shaft terminal of the aerial ropeway showing on the left the new ore bin. The pylons are completed from here to Tolvaddon.

Opposite below: East Pool & Agar Ltd, Taylor's shaft, 1946. The closure of the mine immediately caused problems for the neighbouring South Crofty Mine and they were obliged to take over the 90in pumping engine and continue, at some expense, to pump from an approximate depth of 1,034ft. It was then necessary to erect the surface balance box, shown here, in order to compensate for the bottom box in the shaft, which was under water. The plate beam of North Goonbarrow China clay works former 36in pumping engine was bought for this purpose.

East Pool & Agar Ltd, Taylor's shaft, 1953. The north-west leg of the headgear taken from the bob platform door. This indicates the amount of decay that had endangered the structure. Men continued to be raised and lowered on this headgear until a shorter new headgear was brought into use on 3 September. Twelve days later, the old headgear collapsed!

East Pool & Agar Ltd. Taylor's shaft, 15 September 1953, 4.35 p.m. This dramatic photograph was taken by the late J.H. Trounson, and shows the headgear at the moment it started to collapse. He had just arrived on site and fortunately was carrying his camera.

Above: East Pool & Agar Ltd, Taylor's shaft, 15 September 1953. Taken only minutes after the collapse of the headgear and showing a group of men who had been changing in the dry, some stripped to the waist, and who rushed out to ascertain what had happened. They are here posing for the photographer, J.H. Trounson.

Right: East Pool & Agar Ltd, Taylor's shaft, 1930s. Taken in the 1,600ft cross-cut (North), showing multiple faulting of a quartz and black tourmaline vein. A most unusual example of a fault.

Above: East Pool & Agar Ltd, Taylor's shaft in around 1943, showing the cementation of a dam at the 1,515ft-level cross-cut. This work was undertaken at the expense of South Crofty Mine. When the Second World War broke out, East Pool Mine was on the verge of being abandoned. With the loss of the Malayan tin source to the Japanese, the Ministry of Supply stepped in to keep the mine at work. The management of South Crofty were in no doubt that at the end of hostilities East Pool's closure would be a certainty and its water would affect them. Two dams were constructed, the other one being at the 1,600ft level. The bearded figure, third from the right, is the late Walter Langford, and the late William Saunders is on the extreme right.

Above: East Pool & Agar Ltd, Taylor's shaft, 11 September 1954. Taken inside the house of the 90in pumping engine, from the stairs leading to the middle chamber. Sitting in the settle are the driver and a former miner, the late 'Pop' Uren, smoking a pipe. He had lost his right hand some years previously in an underground accident. The central figure is the late J.H. Trounson. The engine had been kept at work for some years by South Crofty Mine after the closure of East Pool. Although expensive, this had to be done whilst they undertook the necessary precautions against flooding from the East Pool workings. This scene was captured within a few weeks of the final working of the engine.

Opposite below: East Pool & Agar Ltd, Taylor's shaft, *c.* 1928. An experimental mobile tin smelting plant, mentioned earlier in this series. The building was constructed to house the equipment that was on a trailer. It was intended that the smelter would travel from mine to mine to smelt their concentrate. It was not a success and never moved from this site, where it was scrapped. This should not be confused with the 'in mill' experiments, described earlier in this book. In the foreground are pump columns that had been brought from Highburrow East shaft at the Carn Brea Mine.

Other local interest titles published by The History Press

In a county whose wealth came out of the ground, whether as tin, lead, copper or uranium, mining has shaped Cornwall's landscape and people, affecting every aspect of the county's life. Across his *Mining in Cornwall* series, L.J. Bullen shows the development of mining from its earliest times and the impact of continually changing technology.

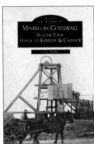 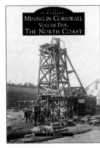 

Mining in Cornwall, Volume One: The Central District
0 7524 1707 X

Mining in Cornwall, Volume Two: The County Explored
0 7524 1707 8

Mining in Cornwall, Volume Three: Penwith and South Kerrier
0 7524 1759 2

Mining in Cornwall, Volume Four: Hayle to Kerrier & Carrick
0 7524 2133 6

Mining in Cornwall, Volume Five: The North Coast
0 7524 2750 4

Mining in Cornwall, Volume Six: Mid-County to the Tamar
0 7524 2878 0

If you are interested in purchasing other books published by The History Press, or in case you have difficulty finding any of our books in your local bookshop, you can also place orders directly through our website:
www.thehistorypress.co.uk